D1095828

VOLUME XII FALL 2011

Important American Paintings

Timeless

QUESTROYAL FINE ART, LLC

903 Park Avenue (at 79th Street), Suite 3A & B, New York, NY 10075

T: (212) 744-3586 F: (212) 585-3828

HOURS: Monday–Friday 10–6, Saturday 10–5 and by appointment

EMAIL: gallery@questroyalfineart.com www.questroyalfineart.com

DESIGN: Malcolm Grear Designers

PRINTING: Meridian Printing

PHOTOGRAPHY: Timothy Pyle, Light Blue Studio

EDITING: Amanda Sparrow

INSIDE FRONT COVER (DETAIL)
Jasper Francis Cropsey (1823–1900), *Autumn in America*, ca. 1860, PLATE 32

INSIDE BACK COVER (DETAIL)
Reginald Marsh (1898–1954), *Beach Scene*, 1953
PLATE 25

All entries written by Louis M. Salerno except PLATE 22, written by André Salerno.

On the Verge of Making the Buy of the Year: High Anxiety in Pursuit of a Masterpiece, written by Brent L. Salerno, falls after PLATE 15.

Contents

Paintings from $100,000 to $195,000

Paintings from $250,000 to $675,000

Paintings above $700,000

Works in the Catalogue

Foreword BY CHLOE HEINS

I may take for granted that I spend the majority of my time surrounded by paintings. Their imagery is my reality. On this particular day, a 360-degree spin in my desk chair spans Maine, Paris, Coney Island beach, the Hudson, Mount Desert Island, the Adirondacks, Alaska, and — my personal favorite — the realm of early American modernism. I am an avid hiker, and on every trail lined with Queen Anne's lace, I think of Burchfield, and when I look at Burchfields, I am reminded of such days spent in nature. Just as it is absurd to imagine isolation from the outside world, it should be equally impossible for us to tolerate life without a daily dose of art.

Art creates a dialogue between us. It is a bridge between our minds and distinctive viewpoints. We recently owned a particularly poignant and unique modernist painting. While it incited a reaction out of many, it was not, on a surface level, sensational or provocative. After viewing this work in the company of many different clients, I began to acknowledge its effect. On one afternoon at an art fair, a woman whom I had never met walked into our booth and went right over to the painting. We stood there together, eyes glued to the wall, talking quietly. After a conversation that covered her first art purchase decades ago to the present moment, her inexplicable draw to this piece, she exclaimed, "Looking at that painting is like eating a piece of chocolate cake!" I laughed at this perfect description, envisioning an identical rich forkful in each of our hands, and felt completely invigorated in the wake of our exchange. While examining and discussing art is something we've grown accustomed to, certain experiences awaken your perspective and increase art's value far beyond a headline-worthy auction record.

In my experience, the art business is about connecting people to art. Forming that connection is, in its simplest form, a type of matchmaking. The more I know about our clients and our paintings, the more competently I can introduce them. As we become better acquainted, I form an understanding of the types of paintings you are attracted to. There is a visible shift in the body language, expression, and mood of the future owner of an artwork when they see it for the first time. To unite them is a privilege and an experience I find infinitely rewarding.

Preface BY LOUIS M. SALERNO

A faded envelope arrives in the mail, postmarked more than one hundred years ago. It is addressed to you. A letter that was written just as innocence was overtaken by invention, and the world irreversibly progressed to the twenty-first century. The intrigue is overwhelming; you need to know what the letter preserves. It could change your life.

I know, I'm at it again, trying to rouse your imagination, but in this catalogue are what could be thought of as forty-four letters — not words in ink on paper, but images in oil on canvas. Although they vary in shape and size, each work should be owned by someone who recognizes its personal and profound message. Which one was meant for you?

Many collectors have confided that they are worried about the state of the world, and this concern has adversely affected their willingness to pursue their passion. They should heed the words of J. Paul Getty: "Nobody ever got rich on a doomsday theory." Consider the collector who came to the gallery not long ago and desperately wanted to buy three expensive paintings. He became increasingly agitated, unable to summon the conviction to complete the sale. I asked him what was his greatest concern. He replied, "Lou, I love the paintings, but everything is so unpredictable. Sometimes it feels like the world is coming to an end." I extended my hand and made this solemn promise: I guaranteed that he would get his money back if the world ended. We laughed long and hard, realizing the absurdity of this sort of thinking. He bought the paintings.

I can be creative, so let me know what trepidations you might have. I will find a similar solution!

Get to Know Questroyal's Founder

Louis's Mind Unzipped—Proceed with Caution!

THE ECONOMIST

Some collectors of contemporary art are willing to suspend the laws of supply and demand so that they may attain a coveted position within a social hierarchy that is determined by the degree to which they most defy economic logic. Price itself then becomes the primary motivation for acquisition.

THE CULTURIST

Our art is a treasure not yet discovered by a society nurtured on neon. We will someday grow tired of toys and become as voracious for truth and beauty.

THE PHILOSOPHER

Thoreau did not want to be on the verge of death only to discover that he had not yet lived. This thought haunts me. How is it possible to live a lifetime and know little or nothing of the very crust of life, its primary force? We live insulated in cities of brick and mortar. Where is the raw scent of earth? Our air is conditioned, and our windows are closed. So I wonder: How much have I really lived?

THE PATRIOT

It's not wise to lose faith in this nation's great resiliency. This is America—survivor of the Revolution, Civil War, Great Depression, social injustice, and two world wars—and through each crisis, no matter what the magnitude, we have triumphed and prospered. Recovery is inevitable; let's not be paralyzed in the present but commence a course of action to be best positioned for the future.

THE SCIENTIST

The nineteenth-century American painting hangs defiantly in the modern home, an oddity in the company of constantly evolving technology. The painting remains unchanged, proving the peculiar validity of Darwin's theory—survival of the fittest.

Main Gallery
Questroyal Fine Art

AMERICAN PAINTING AND ITS TRADITION

Paintings under $100,000

LEFT: **Leon Kroll**, *May at Woodstock*, PLATE 14

RIGHT: **Robert Henri**, *Monhegan, Maine*, PLATE 12

Oscar Bluemner (1867–1938)

PLATE 1 *Downpour*

Watercolor on paper

9 5/8 x 12 1/2 inches (sight size)

Signed lower right: *OFBLÜMNER* (artist's monogram)

This truly fine Bluemner was offered at one of the three major auction houses last fall. I believed it would sell for four times the high estimate and was stunned to acquire it at the middle range of the estimate. My jubilation dissipated quickly as I realized that even with a preponderance of supporting evidence, if I priced the work at what I thought was a fair value, I would appear greedy. But if you will accept the possibility that sometimes the fault lies not in the art but in the market, then perhaps my argument will be convincing.

An auction is subject to the prevailing economic sentiment. Just as companies' stock valuations may rise or fall to extreme levels without justification one month only to return to a sensible valuation the next, works of art are also subject to the trepidations of market makers. Furthermore, what percentage of the total market participants are in the auction room with available funds on sales day?

Charles Darwin believed that all things return to the norm, and on that fall day, the market was far from normal. And if he is right, that will soon change.

Alexander Bower (1875–1952)

PLATE 2 *On the Cape, Near the Purpoodock Club, Maine*

Oil on canvas

25 3/16 x 30 3/16 inches

Signed lower left: *ALEXANDER BOWER*; titled on verso:
ON THE CAPE, NEAR THE PURPOODOCK CLUB

It is impossible to understand how Bower managed to escape any notable fame, but I certainly have not overlooked him. His credentials are common to great artists—exhibitions at the National Academy of Design, Pennsylvania Academy of the Fine Arts, Art Institute of Chicago, and the Corcoran Gallery of Art—and his work merits inclusion in any serious collection.

The painting featured here is simply one of the most exquisitely orchestrated compositions that has ever hung on the walls of my gallery. If I covered the signature on our best winter scenes—those by Mignot, Redfield, and Palmer—I would wager that Bower would command the attention and admiration of our most discerning collectors.

Just as fame inflates the value of paintings, works that must be judged solely on merit are often substantially undervalued. Alexander Bower's On the Cape *will withstand the scrutiny of the harshest critic.*

ALEXANDER BOWER

Charles Ephraim Burchfield (1893–1967)

PLATE 3 *Backyard—Late Winter,* 1916

Watercolor on paper

19 1/2 x 13 5/8 inches (sight size)

Signed and dated lower right: *–C E Burchfield–1916*

PLATE 4 *Dead Trees in Southern Woods,* 1918

Watercolor, gouache, and pencil on paper

12 x 9 inches

Signed lower right: *Chas Burchfield;* signed and dated lower left: *Chas Burchfield 1918*

I was jolted by Blakelock and now, unexpectedly, by Burchfield. There is nothing quite as astounding as the moment when an artwork engages that part of your mind that lets you see natural phenomena you have never before comprehended. It is as if you have a supernatural sensory ability: you are seeing as well as hearing an image. This sounds a bit fantastical, but some of you may or will experience just such a moment.

Burchfield actually invented systems of symbols to visually represent sound, and his inanimate objects were given human emotions. All of his art was designed to transport the viewer to a new level of discovery. He was confident and determined, writing: "It came over me all at once how proud and glad I was that I was 'I'—that my conception of nature was sufficient to me."

Charles Ephraim Burchfield (1893–1967)

PLATE 4 *Dead Trees in Southern Woods,* 1918

Watercolor, gouache, and pencil on paper

12 x 9 inches

Signed lower right: *Chas Burchfield*; signed and dated lower left: *Chas Burchfield 1918*

Both of the watercolors presented here were created within one year of what Burchfield determined was his golden year: 1917. This was the period when "memories of [his] boyhood crowded in upon [him] to make that time also a dream world of the imagination."

In Backyard—Late Winter, 1916, *the artist commingles trees with architectural elements, without undue emphasis on either. The arrangement serves as an example of what Edward Hopper noted about Burchfield's ability to produce an evocative mood by refusing to use any one component "too exclusively."*

In Dead Trees in Southern Woods, 1918, *a thick coppice of trees is represented, with those in the background curved to form peaks like Gothic arches (a symbol of God in nature). Burchfield's interest in nature's divinity and mysticism is unmistakable.*

Chas Burchfield 1918

John William Casilear (1811–1893)

PLATE 5 *Mountain River Landscape,* 1868

Oil on canvas

12 1/4 x 10 1/4 inches

Signed and dated lower right: *JWC* (artist's monogram) *68*

It is normal to think that compelling art is made by the most famous artists; however, fame is chameleon-like, and it is determined most by trends and fashion and least by substance and fact.

Perhaps Mr. Casilear didn't attend chic affairs or command the attention of the Whitneys and Morgans. However, today, it is his art that is in the very best company, found in the halls and parlors of The Metropolitan Museum of Art, The White House, National Gallery of Art, and in so many more of the nation's greatest institutions.

John William Casilear is worthy of any collection and, best of all, the value of his paintings does not exceed the caliber of his talent.

George Cope (1855–1929)

PLATE 6 *Still Life with Berries, Sugar, and Cream Pitcher,* 1916

Oil on canvas mounted on board

12 x 9 1/8 inches

Signed and dated: *GC* (artist's monogram) *'16*

We live in a highly mechanical and technologically obsessed society. Our lives are devoid of the artistry and craftsmanship of men who painstakingly created with their own hands. Those of us who admire such workmanship can benefit from understanding that the perfection attained by perseverance requires a disciplined effort.

The skill necessary to produce still-life paintings of the type George Cope created is considerable. He labored endlessly and once said, "I was eternally sketching and drawing." In 1885, a reviewer of Cope's work commented that "great labor has attended the production of this fine painting, details being carefully observed and the drawing faultless."

The product of great effort should be visible in our homes, as much for ourselves as for our children.

Jasper Francis Cropsey (1823–1900)

PLATE 7 *Landscape with Trees,* 1885

Oil on canvas

7 5/8 x 6 5/16 inches

Signed and dated lower right: *J. F. Cropsey 1885*

In May of this year, two newly discovered paintings by Cropsey were presented for sale at a small auction house in Larchmont, New York. A fifteen-by-twenty-four-inch winter scene fetched $540,500, and a fall picture of the same size sold for $282,000. We were all reminded of Cropsey's incredible appeal and importance as a leading Hudson River school painter. In fact, he was one of only a few such artists who earned an international reputation: he exhibited throughout Europe, won a medal at the London International exhibition, and held audiences with the Queen of England.

We are offering four Cropseys, in several different price ranges. This finely executed small work of his most important subject—autumn in America—is perfect for those who wish to own a prime example at a modest cost. It can be acquired for substantially under the upper limit of this section's price category.

Edward Alfred Cucuel (1875–1954)

PLATE 8 *Two Girls in White Beside a Lake in Autumn*

Oil on canvas

31 9/16 x 31 3/4 inches

Signed lower right: *Cucuel*

To stimulate your interest, I contemplated mentioning Cucuel's superior training under the masters Bouguereau and Gérôme, and further extrapolating on the considerable international recognition Cucuel commanded. But then I got a better idea.

An art dealer could offer many reasons why a painting is worth owning, but none would exceed the sheer pleasure of gazing at a place and time that you would love to experience. The world has changed a great deal in the century or so since this work was created, but perhaps that is exactly why this painting is so compelling to us now. As for myself, I imagine sitting on the bench at the lake's edge as I await the company of the two lovely ladies. Some things never change.

Thomas Doughty (1793–1856)

PLATE 9 *Sublime Landscape*

Oil on canvas mounted to board

14 1/8 x 17 5/8 inches

Signed lower left: *DOUGHTY*

It's time to consider the work of Thomas Doughty as on a par with that of Thomas Cole, the recognized leader of the Hudson River school. Cole has been credited with the style and philosophical underpinning of America's most indigenous art; however, new scholarship and recently discovered historical documentation indicate that Doughty's influence may have been underestimated.

In 1825, Rembrandt Peale wrote to Thomas Jefferson to recommend Doughty for the position of art instructor at the University of Virginia. The artist's notoriety and stature continued to grow, and perhaps we, as modern collectors, should heed the words of the editor of the Knickerbocker Magazine, *who wrote in 1848: "Doughty's pictures and Cole's pictures should be placed apart from the rest. We all admit them to be our masters; Cole in one style and Doughty in another."*

Sublime Landscape *is an exquisite example of the awe and wonder that America's earliest painters experienced as they explored the untamed country.*

William James Glackens (1870–1938)

PLATE 10 *Four Fruits*

Oil on panel

9 13/16 x 13 13/16 inches

Signed lower right: *W. Glak* (illegible);
verso: *Susanna without the Elders*

Imagine a child with artistic inclinations who has the good fortune of befriending John Sloan in high school, having Thomas Anshutz as his instructor, and sharing a studio with Robert Henri! This elite circle of influence fostered the great talent of William Glackens.

Great artists build upon the work of those who came before them, and Constance Schwartz, author of The Shock of Modernism in America, *observed that Glackens, "influenced by Manet and Renoir, . . . adapted a palette of richer, brighter and sharper color, and his paintings became an extension of impressionist principles with a new vigor and sparkle."*

Here, Glackens—by allowing the small flowers to fall away from the tabletop—suggests atmosphere by combining space with a sense of movement. He effectively creates the illusion that his fruits are alive within a life-sustaining environment in the confines of the canvas. Is it a painting of a still life or a portal through which viewers glimpse a separate, vibrant life?

I urge you to consider this progressive and individualized work by an artist who was a founding member of The Eight, the group of "radicals" who broke away from the establishment and gained fame at the pivotal 1913 Armory Show.

George Henry Hall (1825–1913)

PLATE 11 *Still Life with Flowers,* 1861

Oil on artist's board

12 1/16 x 10 1/16 inches

Signed and dated lower left: *G.H. Hall. '61*

One day, a collector with a fine eye visited the gallery with an interesting painting under his arm. The work had never been cleaned and was so dirty that my fingers turned black from examining it. There was no way to discern the color, but the form was intriguing and the George Hall signature visible. It had been a long week, and my unending desire to buy paintings had resulted in a spending spree that even I could not justify. With regret, I told him to offer the work to my colleagues and if no one bought it to let me know. He was halfway to the elevator before I shouted for him to return—I could not resist. George Hall was a superior still-life painter, and I knew the picture would be stunning after it was cleaned. I wrote the check.

I'm so thankful that this gem did not get away. It boasts an elegance—but not a price—common to the great still lifes. As with many refined nineteenth-century paintings, this work may not elicit the attention of socialites, but when it hangs on your wall, you will know it's good and that's what matters most.

Robert Henri (1865–1929)

PLATE 12 *Monhegan, Maine*

Pastel on paper mounted to board

20 x 14 1/8 inches

Signed lower right: *Robert Henri*

Have you forgotten the lure of the woods? As a child, I wandered on forest paths, summoning the courage to venture deeper and imagining what I might discover. Sometimes it was as dark as night at midday and the sounds were unlike any I had ever heard.

Robert Henri, leader of the Ashcan school, may have rediscovered the same childlike wonder as he explored Cathedral Woods on Monhegan Island, Maine. Dr. Norman Geske writes: "The extraordinary pastels from Monhegan [are] pictures whose creation does not seem to have been rationalized to an excess. In each of these works [Henri's] response to place, to atmosphere, to structure of space [is] direct and potent in its intensity."

Art has so many purposes, and, in this instance, it allows me to reexperience my boyhood. Fragments of memory somehow come into focus, and I get a sense of the wonder I once knew. Nothing but art, though some might argue drugs, can do this.

George Inness (1825–1894)

PLATE 13 *Study for the Catskills,* ca. 1875

Oil on paper laid down on canvas

9 3/16 x 12 7/16 inches

Thomas Cole journeyed to New York's Catskill Mountains in 1825 and returned from the haunting wilderness to create what are considered to be the first Hudson River school paintings. For the next half-century, nearly every major American landscape painter made the same pilgrimage.

The Hudson River school isn't a reference to a place; the term describes the style of America's most indigenous landscapes. Since it all began in the Catskills, serious collectors always seek images of this hallowed region, but those who prefer their art to have an edge look to the work of the fiercely independent and rebellious George Inness. He refined a style and technique to suggest unseen emotion, taking total and radical control of his paint to achieve his aim—art for art's sake. Widely acknowledged as a genius, he built a foundation upon which the likes of Pollock, Rothko, and De Kooning would expand.

What you feel when you gaze at Study for the Catskills *is how you must judge this painting.*

Leon Kroll (1884–1974)

PLATE 14 *May at Woodstock*, 1924

Oil on canvas

20 1/4 x 24 3/16 inches

Signed and dated lower right: *Leon Kroll 1924*;
titled and signed on verso: *May at Woodstock, Leon Kroll*

In 1901, Winslow Homer noticed Leon Kroll—who was then just a teenager and a member of the Art Students League under the tutelage of John Twachtman—and encouraged him to pursue a painting career. Homer was a perceptive judge of talent, as Kroll went on to garner fame and honors as a premier painter.

Throughout the 1920s, Woodstock was a mecca for American artists. They immersed themselves in the vast collective creativity and pristine natural environment of the bohemian community, and their talents flourished. Alexander Brook, a prominent New York artist, wrote, "Probably one of the greatest moments in the lives of some came when George Bellows, Robert Henri, and Leon Kroll agreed to spend a summer in Woodstock." Kroll created some of his greatest works within its boundaries, and in 1924, amid surging artistic activity, he painted May at Woodstock, *a remarkable example of his individual and uninhibited style.*

Anna Mary Robertson "Grandma" Moses (1860–1961)

PLATE 15 *Now We Can Skate*

Oil on board

5 11/16 x 7 9/16 inches

Signed lower left: *MOSES.*; titled and inscribed on verso: *now we can Skate, no 1357,*

The old lady from rural America had something to say about life and the great truths she found at home in her simple and innocent surroundings. All of life's goodness—the things that money can't buy—are found in her paintings.

The complex ideology of a great artist's work may exceed the grasp of many, but the least among us need only to look back at our own experience to understand and cherish an original Grandma Moses. With as much name recognition as Homer or Whistler—and more American than apple pie—Grandma Moses created folksy, unsophisticated imagery that illuminated wholesome truths, and yet her paintings are the very highest form of art.

In her own wise words: "I look back on my life like a good day's work, it was done and I feel satisfied with it. I was happy and contented, I knew nothing better and made the best out of what life offered. And life is what we make it, always has been, always will be."

MOSES.

On the Verge of Making the Buy of the Year: High Anxiety in Pursuit of a Masterpiece

By Brent L. Salerno

I have been a part of many acquisitions over the years, but I've experienced nothing as exciting as our most recent purchase.

The painting was brought to our attention in a most unlikely way. Although we spend a good portion of our days scouring the papers, reading e-mails, sifting through actual mail, checking Web sites, and taking phone calls from people offering paintings for sale, that is not how this work was discovered.

An old family friend noticed the painting in a London auction. He recognized the artist's name from one of our online catalogues. This was a sale of European and Russian art, and after quickly browsing the lots, I realized that it was the only American work offered—a great opportunity for an American dealer. However, the sale was the very next day.

With sixteen hours to act and no time to fly to London to inspect the painting, I contacted the auction house and asked for a condition report and as many high-resolution images as they would be willing to provide. Aside from a small repaired tear on the right side—a minor blip for a sixty-seven-inch canvas—it was in perfect condition. My interest escalated to pure excitement. This painting was likely the artist's masterpiece, and we were possibly the only serious buyer aware of it. I held my breath at the thought. I immediately set up a phone line, relieved to know there was still one available. There were just fourteen hours left. All I could do was wait and worry about what might go wrong. I anticipated a sleepless night, knowing that we were on the verge of making the buy of the year.

Morning slowly came. I dressed, poured a cup of coffee, and got into my car for my daily commute into the city. As I was sitting in traffic, slowly making my way over the George Washington Bridge, I couldn't help but think that someone else could be on to this painting. Would there be a bidding war? The stress started to get to me.

I got to my desk and logged on to the auction Web site. It was 10 AM at the gallery, but it was 3 PM in London. The auction was underway. I determined that a call would come within the hour. I waited.

Forty-five minutes later, the phone rang. Lou and I locked ourselves in his office to prevent any distractions. The time had come! The auctioneer was looking for an opening bid. He received it on the floor. There was a bidder in the room! How high would we have to go? We made the next bid, prepared to bid many more times. But, as quickly as it started, the auction ended, and the bang of the gavel echoed through the phone. We bought the painting with only one bid! We were the only serious buyer aware of the painting. It would have sold for many times more, had it been in any significant American sale.

It's back in the United States, where it was originally painted and where it belongs. It missed our catalogue deadline by three days. You will likely find it hanging in my office at the time of this printing.

I can honestly say that it looks even more impressive in person. Ask me about it.

Full Image and Information
Now Available

Paintings from $100,000 to $195,000

Guy Carleton Wiggins, *View of Fifth Avenue, Winter*, PLATE 26

Albert Bierstadt (1830–1902)

PLATE 16 *Sea and Sky*

Oil on paper mounted on board

14 1/8 x 18 1/4 inches

Signed lower right: *ABierstadt* (artist's monogram)

Misconceptions exist even for the most prominent artists. The idea that Bierstadt's genius is best expressed by his monumental western landscapes is simply untrue. While those vast views were responsible for the artist's fame and wealth, the works that most exhibit the depth of his talent are his smaller but supremely creative and forward-thinking oils.

The creation of an artist who was well ahead of his time, Sea and Sky *is accurately described as being at the crossroads of abstraction and impressionism. In these unique visions, Bierstadt abandoned his pursuit of wealth to nourish his innermost artistic sensibility.*

We have included this painting in two different critically reviewed gallery shows. Twice it commanded the attention of a reviewer and was identified as a standout.

Elizabeth Wilson of ARTnews *called it "a vaporous oil sketch that verges on abstraction, depicting billowing clouds above a lonely beach."*

Mona Molarsky, also of ARTnews, *wrote,* "Sea and Sky *(n.d.), distinguished by intense blues and impulsive brushwork, could hold its own against a Monet."*

Bierstadt

Thomas Cole (1801–1848)

PLATE 17 *On Catskill Creek*, 1836

Oil on canvas

20 5/8 x 15 11/16 inches

Signed, inscribed, and dated on verso panel:
Thomas Cole Catskill 1836

I exited the Academia in Florence, Italy, feeling elated. It was not Michelangelo's David *but rather his unfinished* Slaves, *lining the approach to his masterpiece, that roused my interest. They were so poignant, I thought that they would have been diminished by any further degree of completion. Why Michelangelo left so many sculptures unfinished is a question that has confounded scholars for centuries.*

The great American painter Thomas Cole was also inclined to leave many of his paintings unfinished, and I am more attracted to them than to many of his finished works. Is it possible that there is a point during the creative process at which an artist achieves his highest ambition and instinctively knows that any continuation would dilute his desired effect? After many centuries of debate, I doubt that there will ever be a consensus of opinion, and I also doubt the need for one.

Finished or not, Cole's On Catskill Creek, *a possible view of his home and studio, is for that confident collector who will always consider a work of art perfect and complete if it enlivens his imagination.*

Samuel Colman (1832–1920)

PLATE 18 *Morning*, 1859

Oil on canvas

15 1/4 x 24 3/16 inches

Signed and dated lower right: *S. Colman '59*

There are far too many collectors whose focus on contemporary art has led them to reject the beautiful for the imponderable. The most desired objects are those that look the least like art—and their stunning price tags offer a passport for social entrée, if not institutionalization!

For these collectors, the motivation to acquire a given work is influenced less by an emotional connection and more by the obtuse logic of dealers and scholars. Paintings of great poetic sensitivity, of the type Mr. Colman dedicated his life to create, are dismissed because of the false assumption that sophisticated art cannot be beautiful.

The day I see a hedge funder sipping cocktails on his yacht, adrift in the swamp adjacent to the sewage plant, which was the subject of the last painting he acquired, I will raise the white flag.

I implore all of you who appreciate beauty to ponder Samuel Colman's Morning.

Jasper Francis Cropsey (1823–1900)

PLATE 19 *A Cabin on Greenwood Lake,* 1879

Oil on canvas

9 7/16 x 16 3/8 inches

Signed and dated lower right: *J. F. Cropsey 1879*

I rank Cropsey among the best of the top-tier Hudson River school artists. Four of his paintings, in various price ranges, are included in this catalogue. The art market is recovering quickly, but we are still below peak levels. Now is the perfect time to add the great painter of America's autumn to your collection.

A Cabin on Greenwood Lake *was painted very near Cropsey's home in Warwick, New York. The small bridge and winding path lead to a log cabin where someone waits at the door. We need to reacquaint ourselves with the simple joy of living in nature's unspoiled neighborhood. This idyllic canvas is therapeutic and boasts the same or a greater degree of efficacy as any modern antidepressant. It's also a reminder that we are drifting too far from the truth.*

Régis François Gignoux (1814–1882)

PLATE 20 *Long Island in 1850*

Oil on canvas

40 1/16 x 62 1/16 inches

Signed and dated lower center: *R.Gignoux 1850*

I stood before this Gignoux in preparation to write this entry, and, unexpectedly, my imagination was flooded with a sensation that—even for me as a creative type—seemed a bit far-fetched. My inclination was to avoid describing it for fear of being accused of resorting to premeditated fabrication in order to provoke a sale. But what I sensed was truthful, so I decided to take a chance.

Long Island in 1850 *is a grand canvas measuring sixty-two inches across. It feels like a panoramic window that reveals a vaguely familiar, perhaps forgotten world. But for a fleeting moment, this other world is alive again. It is as if upon touching the presumed window pane, one could feel and maybe even hear the distant hum of a separate life in another time. I wonder: What reality might remain, should the glass veil separating them shatter?*

It's that good. Come see it with your own eyes and imagination.

Winslow Homer (1836–1910)

PLATE 21

Head of a Young Girl, 1874

Pencil and gouache on paper

5 1/8 x 4 1/4 inches (sight size)

Signed and dated lower left: *W.H. -74*

Head of a Young Girl in Profile

Pencil and gouache on paper

5 1/4 x 4 7/16 inches (sight size)

We own art because it nourishes us in many ways, some of which we might not even comprehend. And for those of us who wish to spend more time enjoying something rather than attending to its care and maintenance, art will be that rare possession that will not own us. It will never require anything other than admiration.

For collectors who seek a simple truth and a precious beauty, I can think of no better choice than this pencil and gouache pair. Abigail Booth Gerdts describes the images in the Winslow Homer catalogue raisonné: "The drawings are highly finished independent works . . . these drawings and the related oil are exceptional in having the particularity in facial detail which marks them as examples of portraiture." The related oil she references is in the collection of the Yale University Art Gallery.

h. H. -74

Rockwell Kent (1882–1971)

PLATE 22 *Alaska,* 1919

Oil on board

12 x 13 7/8 inches

Signed, titled, and dated lower right:
Rockwell Kent. Alaska, 1919.

Written by André Salerno

As I sit here, deep within the ever-pulsating heart of the concrete jungle, thinking of ways to make more money, I know the great artist, author, traveler, and thinker Rockwell Kent would not have approved.

He would, however, take solace in the fact that when I view his Alaska, *I can escape the monotony, the materialism, and the utter madness that living and working in modern civilization often entails.*

If you look at many of Kent's paintings, you will be reminded of that other world, the one of natural beauty that only exists for leisurely souls brave enough to truly experience it—the one that so many of us will only know briefly, if at all, throughout the course of our busy lives.

This is the world that Kent found in 1918 and 1919. He ran away from the fortune, fame, and notoriety he'd found in New York to meld himself with Alaska's seas, mountains, and skies. The results of his bold foray into the unknown are paintings like this one.

Now, a fortunate collector can glimpse the grandeur that Kent experienced—without ever leaving the comfort of home.

Rockwell Kent, Alaska, 1919.

Leon Kroll (1884–1974)

PLATE 23 *Monhegan*, 1913

Oil on panel

15 1/16 x 19 1/2 inches

Signed lower right: *Kroll*; titled, dated, and signed on verso: *Monhegan 1913 Leon Kroll*

Kroll exhibited at the historic Armory Show of 1913 and, at the urging of George Bellows, traveled to Monhegan Island, Maine, in the summer of that year. There he painted this and other superb images. It was a pivotal time in Kroll's career, and this work deserves consideration as among the finest examples from his oeuvre.

I first noticed this painting in a colleague's booth at an art show. I decided that if it did not sell, I would make an offer at the very last moment, resorting to a strategy collectors often use and dealers dislike. It was fun to change roles, but the dealer said he "loved the painting too much to accept my offer."

Over the next several months, I fine-tuned my proposal and bought too many drinks and dinners for a dealer who was as obstinate as I was eager. Sometimes the acquisition of a great painting necessitates odd behavior.

I did what it took to buy it, and I have no regrets and neither should you. I have done all the begging and pleading; you merely have to write the check.

Ernest Lawson (1873–1939)

PLATE 24 *Inwood, Upper Washington Heights*

Oil on canvas

17 3/4 x 21 5/16 inches

Signed lower left: *LAWSON*

It wasn't the city or the country that most captured Ernest Lawson's interest—his fascination was at the convergence of both. The city was expanding, reaching outward; the rural landscape was under assault. It was at the outskirts, the line of demarcation, that the transformation was most potent, and it was here that Lawson placed his easel. His art reminds us to contemplate change.

Lawson's Inwood, Upper Washington Heights *is a perfect example of his most poignant work. He shows no allegiance to either the city's urban onslaught or the rural countryside, as they each shimmer in gemlike fashion. It's a dynamic time, and this painting might best be described as "a beautiful turbulence."*

It is no wonder, then, that the February 7, 1907, issue of The Sun *quotes the leader of The Eight, Robert Henri, as saying, "This man is the biggest we have had since Winslow Homer."*

Reginald Marsh (1898–1954)

PLATE 25 *Beach Scene*, 1953

Mixed media on board

19 1/4 x 23 7/16 inches (sight size)

Signed and dated lower right: *Reginald Marsh 1953*;
Second composition on verso, signed and dated lower right:
Reginald Marsh 1951

verso

The young cartoonist with a keen eye for the human body, especially that of women, was irrevocably intoxicated by the city's relentless stimulation, and it infiltrated his every sense. He was not in New York very long before he was sent on assignment to a place where he would return nearly every year of his life: the Coney Island beach. There he found throngs of half-naked bodies interwoven and contorted in hedonistic leisure, and he gave form to this visual ecstasy in the art that would make him famous.

In Marsh's own words, "[C]rowds of people in all directions, in all positions, without clothing, moving—like the great compositions of Michelangelo and Rubens. . . ."

The critics soon began calling his females "Marsh Ladies," and his friend and earliest collector, William Benton, called them "Marshans" because "no other words describe them."

Marsh was prophetic: "When they look like people you never knew, almost like people who never lived . . . then my pictures will sell."

I find myself thinking about this fascinating view of Coney Island frequently. It's just so original—so American!

Reginald Marsh 1953

Guy Carleton Wiggins (1883–1962)

PLATE 26 *View of Fifth Avenue, Winter*

Oil on canvas

16 1/16 x 12 1/8 inches

Signed lower left: *Guy Wiggins*

Those of us who collect Wiggins can hardly walk along Fifth Avenue, Broadway, or Wall Street without seeing some hint of the artist everywhere. The image of his canvas held in our memories is fully reconciled with the vision we see along the streets, and we feel confident that he painted truthfully.

Wiggins was prolific and has become so familiar that we tend to misjudge his true ability. He was the youngest artist ever to be represented in the permanent collection of The Metropolitan Museum of Art, and his best work has earned its place in nearly every major American public and private collection.

View of Fifth Avenue, Winter *is an elegant scene of city life early in the last century, and it deserves to be in the company of great impressionist paintings.*

Irving R. Wiles (1861–1948)

PLATE 27 *Schooners at Anchor*

Oil on canvas

20 3/8 x 29 1/4 inches

Signed lower right: *Irving R Wiles*

I continue to emphasize the importance of timing. The value of assets fluctuates as a consequence of perceptions, most of which are based on emotions that have little to do with fact.

In May of 2009, this exceptional painting by Wiles was offered at auction. I was certain of three things:

1. *His work was consistently rising at auction.*
2. *This example was of very high quality.*
3. *It was the wrong time to offer it for sale and the right time to buy it.*

We were in about the most severe stage of the recession, which—as long as there would be a tomorrow—had little to do with the true value of the painting.

I made one of my best purchases that spring day, and auction comparables substantiate a valuation that is nearly twice as high as our asking price.

CENTURIES-OLD DISCOVERY

No Taxes and *No* Maintenance

Land Guaranteed Forever Perfect

A gardener's paradise framed by waterfront views.

see PLATE 44

Not far from town. Charming village location.

see PLATE 14

They Called it ART

Thanks to an extraordinary discovery centuries ago, it is possible to forever possess the most incredible vistas and sunsets, the most idyllic lakes and mountains, without ever having to pay taxes or maintenance. There will never be any risk of environmental damage or adverse weather.

Your property is absolutely guaranteed to remain forever perfect.

The best oceanfront property in today's market.

see PLATE 39

Pristine Adirondack lake view. Year-round enjoyment.

see PLATE 18

Paintings from $250,000 to $675,000

LEFT: **Alfred Thompson Bricher**, *Seascape: Sunset,* PLATE 30

RIGHT: **Martin Johnson Heade**, *Newburyport, Massachusetts,* PLATE 35

George Wesley Bellows (1882–1925)

PLATE 28 *The Rich Water,* 1913

Oil on panel

14 3/4 x 19 1/8 inches

Signed lower right: *Geo Bellows*; inscribed on verso:
R YG + B / THE RICH WATER / GEO BELLOWS / 146 E 19 NY / A 180

Drawn to the underbelly of a young America, Bellows discovered the art that gave him purpose on the grimy streets of the city and among the characters at the illegal boxing matches in the back rooms of seedy taverns. His brush was like a scalpel piercing the surface to uncover the raw and unambiguous truth that the nation so desperately needed to understand.

On Monhegan Island, the mighty Atlantic pounded the shores with an unending and rhythmic intensity. Bellows's artistic powers surged as he absorbed the potent and unaltered essence of the ocean. The paintings he created there responded in bold rudimental color and form; the artist was forever a celebrant of the truth.

The world has recognized Bellows's astounding talent. In 1999, his Polo Crowd *sold at Sotheby's for $27,702,500. In fact, ten of his paintings have exceeded one million dollars at auction.*

Thomas Hart Benton (1889–1975)

PLATE 29 *Missouri Spring,* 1938 (Study for *Spring on the Missouri,* 1945)

Oil on board

7 15/16 x 10 3/8 inches

Signed and dated lower left: *Benton '38*; titled on verso: *Missouri Spring*

The emotion and depth of feeling of Benton's work are so profound that I'm sometimes inclined to look away. His art absorbed all that it required from his life—the ecological tragedy, the human hardship, and the pure and simple lifestyle of an honest people—and it rises to the surface of his canvas with so much potency that one has an overwhelming urge to stand up and applaud. Roger Medearis, his student, recalls Benton remarking, "As an artist you have to give what it takes. If you aren't ready to starve for art, you'd better quit now."

Henry Adams, a prominent Benton scholar and catalogue committee member commented, "So far as I know, this is the first time Benton portrayed lightning in a painting." He believes that it is a study for the North Carolina Museum of Art's version, and he further stated, "This is a superb example of Benton's work from the prime moment of his career."

If I were not the seller and you asked my advice, I would implore you to sell whatever you must and endure any financial strain to buy great Benton paintings. I will do the same.

Alfred Thompson Bricher (1837–1908)

PLATE 30 *Seascape: Sunset*

Oil on canvas

27 1/8 x 50 1/4 inches

Signed lower left: *ATBricher.*

A dealer takes considerable risk when declaring a painting a masterpiece. His opinion, perhaps more so than the actual work, is subjected to a higher degree of scrutiny than is customary. I say, without reservation or hesitation, that Bricher's Seascape: Sunset *is a masterpiece.*

Brilliant in its composition and finely nuanced light, the work shows a natural wonder that is cohesively rendered and fully realized on a grand scale. The artist was philosophically in harmony with the transcendental movement, and this image is a visual re-creation of its central precepts.

To best understand Bricher's vision, one need only to turn to the words of Ralph Waldo Emerson:

"From the earth, as a shore, I look out into that silent sea. I seem to partake its rapid transformations: the active enchantment reaches my dust, and I dilate and conspire with the morning wind."

Jasper Francis Cropsey (1823–1900)

PLATE 31 *Gates of the Hudson*

Oil on canvas

20 1/4 x 30 5/16 inches

Signed lower left: *J. F. Cropsey*

Timing is an odd thing. For most of us, the present is never quite the right time to take advantage of an opportunity. Yet the great irony is, as we look back from some future date, there never seems to be as good a time as the present.

The works most coveted by Hudson River school collectors are images of the majestic Hudson and, at this very moment, you can acquire a major view of considerable scale at a price that is less than half the auction record for a Cropsey painting of a similar location.

The time is now—the only known vaccine for regret is foresight.

Jasper Francis Cropsey (1823–1900)

PLATE 32 *Autumn in America,* ca. 1860

Oil on canvas

15 1/8 x 24 1/8 inches

Signed lower left: *J. F. Cropsey.*; titled and signed
on verso: *Autumn in America / J.F. Cropsey*

This is one of two canvases by Cropsey that were recently discovered. They were not found in a hidden corner of a great mansion but on the walls of a family's playroom, and for decades they survived Ping-Pong games and assorted childhood mischief. I myself learned of nature's wonder from two simple prints in my grandmother's home. What might an imaginative child have discovered while playing among two masterpieces by Cropsey?

The New York Times *reported that the owner's mother died in 2010, and an estate company offered $250 for the pair. The owner wisely had them appraised, and they sold at auction for a total of just under $900,000. Dr. Kenneth Maddox of the Newington-Cropsey Foundation remarked that "these are two of the more exciting paintings that have surfaced."*

I am proud to offer Autumn in America*, which was created during what is universally deemed the artist's best period. There are many great Cropseys, but this must be considered as among the finest he ever painted.*

Asher B. Durand (1796–1886)

PLATE 33 *Pastoral Landscape*, 1866

Oil on canvas

18 3/4 x 29 1/16 inches

Signed and dated lower right: *ABDurand 1866*

In 2005, Asher B. Durand's Kindred Spirits *sold for $35,000,000. The art world was stunned by the staggering sum and lamented New York City's loss of the tour de force.*

Clients often ask why Hudson River school pictures don't command the megamillion-dollar prices paid for contemporary works. There are many other paintings like Kindred Spirits *that would attain such levels, but these masterpieces are closely held by museums and prominent collectors and are rarely offered for sale. Similar examples cannot be created to capitalize on the dynamics of the market; their creators are forever lost to posterity.*

David Lawall, the foremost Durand scholar, recognized what he thought was "an inventive synthesis of sensation, knowledge and recollections" in the artist's work. Linda Ferber, former curator at the Brooklyn Museum and director of the New-York Historical Society, substantiates such active creativity: "[Durand] was also acknowledged in his day for certain pictorial types and innovations (the pastoral landscape and the vertical forest interior) that were widely influential...."

Look deeper into Durand's Pastoral Landscape *— view it as a mindscape — to fully grasp all it offers.*

Martin Johnson Heade (1819–1904)

PLATE 35 *Newburyport, Massachusetts,* ca. 1880–1890

Oil on canvas

10 3/8 x 20 5/16 inches

If I were to ask collectors for their wish list, the top five, I would bet that a luminous Heade landscape would be very near the top of nearly everyone's list.

I have often stressed the importance of the test of time. For three centuries, collectors, scholars, critics, and the public have praised Heade's incredible marsh scenes.

In 1870, author and critic Henry T. Tuckerman declared, "None of our painters has a more refined sense of beauty, or a more delicate feeling for color."

A 1965 headline in The Washington Post *proclaimed, "Martin Heade painted like Thoreau wrote."*

And in 2001, New York Times *art critic Ken Johnson had this to say: "Martin Johnson Heade has been called the Vermeer of nineteenth-century American painting. To be sure, his luminous, awesomely spacious landscapes may seem a far cry from the Delft master's intimate interiors, but like the latter's, Heade's paintings have a magical lucidity and an enigmatic psychology that continue to captivate the eyes and haunt the minds of modern viewers."*

George Inness (1825–1894)

PLATE 36 *Etretat,* 1892

Oil on canvas

29 7/8 x 45 inches

Signed and dated lower left: *G. Inness 1892*;
inscribed on verso label: *No. 33 Etretat Normandy, 1892 30 x 45*

I was invited to a mansion somewhere north of Manhattan, and the small Frederic Church in my possession was likely to become the next acquisition of one of the most profoundly passionate collectors I have ever known.

He was mesmerized by the small Church, and I was struck by the grand Inness that hung in his elegant dining hall. The painting was the most creative work I had ever seen by one of America's most inventive nineteenth-century masters. With little hope of success, I simply said, "I will trade my Church for your Inness." Because the latter was about six times larger than the former, I emphasized the considerable amount of wall space he would gain.

It was a persuasive point, and so here it is—one of Inness's most celebrated paintings. Its texture quivers as a result of skillful scumbling and glazing, an absolute masterpiece of technique. We have compiled more than twenty pages of research on this painting, but space allows us to share only a few excerpts:

> "It expresses . . . so much and leaves so lively a play to the imagination."
>
> —*The New York Times,* 1894

> "[P]ushed to great perfection . . . a superb and perfect example of the craft of the master."
>
> —Elliot Daingerfield, noted Inness scholar, 1911

George Inness (1825–1894)

PLATE 37 *Palisades on the Hudson*

Oil on canvas

20 1/8 x 30 1/8 inches

Signed lower right: *G. Inness*

Each month, millions of travelers cross the George Washington Bridge and confront the majestic bluffs of the Palisades. Many more pass by on yachts and ferries as they traverse the Hudson River. Witness to fierce revolutionary battles and unaltered by the perpetual assault of storms blowing in from the Atlantic, the cliffs stand ever vigilant as the mighty sentinels of the nation's most vibrant metropolis.

George Inness, perhaps the most ethereally inclined of our greatest artists, could not resist the lure of the indomitable bluffs. The very spirit of the Palisades is visible in the dense and timeless atmosphere that takes precedence over even the most basic detail.

Astute collectors understand the value of site-specific paintings, but some places are more valuable than others. With an audience of nearly twenty million people nearby and the Hudson River as a watery conveyor, the Palisades could not have more exposure or appeal.

William Trost Richards (1833–1905)

PLATE 39 *Coastal Scene*

Oil on canvas

28 1/8 x 48 1/8 inches

Signed and dated indistinctly, lower left: *Wm. T. Richards.*

Of the many outstanding American nineteenth-century artists, Richards has emerged as the group's great coastal painter. His panoramic views of the ocean, in all its varying moods, are rendered so truthfully, it is nearly impossible not to gaze at them in absolute awe. His daughter said that he would stand quietly in the surf for hours and hours to gain a greater understanding of its rhythms and colors. Without unnecessary embellishment or device, his painted image commands the attention of anyone who is mesmerized by the power and mystery of the sea.

I have more than four hundred paintings in the gallery, but there is room for only one behind my desk. This is the work that hangs above me. Every client who comes into my office faces it. I can offer no greater testimony to my faith in its quality.

More proof that Richards's best work is worthy of this degree of honor: Christie's successfully sold another of the artist's remarkable paintings in May 2011 for more than $1,650,000, establishing a new auction record for the artist.

Paintings above $700,000

LEFT: **Childe Hassam**, *Hollyhocks, Isle of Shoals*, PLATE 44

RIGHT: **Childe Hassam**, *Looking over Frenchman's Bay at Green Mountain*, PLATE 42

Marsden Hartley (1877–1943)

PLATE 41 *Mount Katahdin, Snow Storm,* 1942

Oil on masonite

30 x 39 15/16 inches

Signed and dated lower right: *MH / 42*

*"I have achieved the 'sacred' pilgrimage to Ktaadn [*sic*]. I feel as if I have seen God for the first time—I find him so nonchalantly solemn."*

—Marsden Hartley to Adelaid Kuntz

We present the great modernist Marsden Hartley's masterful rendering of his beloved Mt. Katahdin, Maine, the mountain that inspired generations of artists and writers, including Frederic Church and Henry David Thoreau.

Very near the peak and in the throes of a mighty blizzard, we witness the fierce power of nature. It is not terror that we experience as much as awe, which enlivens our spirit and imagination.

The painting's grand scale, desirable date, and important subject matter establish it as rare and valuable for any collector of modern art. The fact that it is offered in this price category should make it nearly irresistible.

Childe Hassam (1859–1935)

PLATE 42 *Looking over Frenchman's Bay at Green Mountain,* 1896

Oil on canvas

26 5/16 x 35 7/8 inches

Signed and dated lower right: *Childe Hassam 1896*

Mount Desert has always inspired America's greatest artists. We are fortunate to have two views of an island so cherished by a nation. Both canvases are of virtually the same size and were painted in the same year by the same artist.

Looking over Frenchman's Bay at Green Mountain, *1896, was previously owned by the Pennsylvania Academy of the Fine Arts and was exhibited at no less than seven museums. Hassam deftly exposes the very essence of Cadillac Mountain and nearby Ironbound Island by rejecting both time and detail. His meticulous handling minimizes structure, resulting in an image suspended so precariously that viewers dare not look away. Noted scholar John Wilmerding wrote of this painting, "[It] is a virtual American Impressionist's reprise of Cole's first great painting of Island scenery from 1845."*

This sensational effort, owned and displayed by the nation's best museums, is worthy of any serious collection.

Childe Hassam

Childe Hassam (1859–1935)

PLATE 43 *Frenchman's Bay, Mount Desert,* 1896

Oil on canvas

26 1/8 x 36 1/4 inches

Signed and dated lower right: *Childe Hassam·1896*;
titled, signed, and dated on verso: *Frenchman's Bay C.H. 1896*

Formerly in the possession of artistic visionaries Newman Montross and the Milch Galleries, Frenchman's Bay, Mount Desert*, 1896, demonstrates the magnitude and range of Hassam's imagination. Whereas* Looking over Frenchman's Bay at Green Mountain *is a pensive celebration of a beloved island, this highly charged image hints at the energy and inspiration that artists and writers found there. The two works date from the same year, but here we see a different Hassam; forward-thinking and moving toward an expressionist style, he commands his brush across thirty-six inches of canvas and advances his art by at least as many years. He risks the rejection of his contemporary audience but creates an art that will resonate for the ages.*

So you, as the discerning collector, may have a difficult choice: Which Hassam should you choose? Of course, the only correct answer is both!

Childe Hassam (1859–1935)

PLATE 44 *Hollyhocks, Isle of Shoals,* 1902

Pastel on paper

17 7/8 x 22 1/16 inches

Signed and dated lower left: *Childe Hassam. 1902*

*With impeccable credentials—extensive provenance, exhibitions at four major museums, and several pages of literary references—*Hollyhocks, Isle of Shoals, *1902, is certainly one of the most important works we have ever offered.*

The nation's most revered impressionist has captured the exquisite beauty of his most cherished subject: Celia Thaxter's garden. I agree with David Park Curry's assessment: "Hassam's pastel captures the magical, detached quality of the garden plot, set on a hill overlooking the ocean."

Seldom can I provide more compelling evidence of an object's worth. In 2008, another work on paper by Hassam, of the same subject, sold at Sotheby's for $2,505,000. This larger view is offered at less than half the price of the comparable image.

Childe Hassam 1902

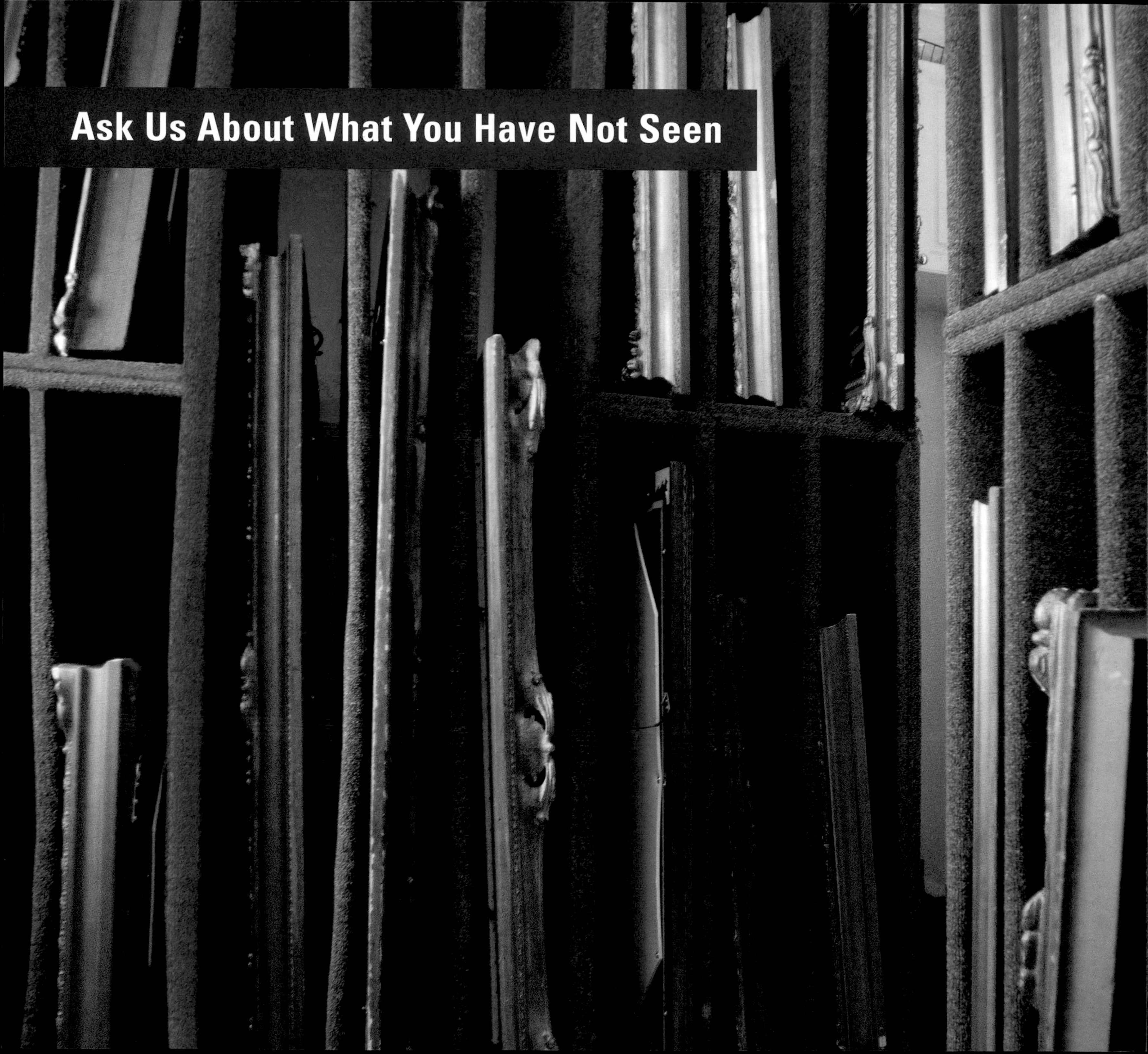
Ask Us About What You Have Not Seen

And Take Another Look

PLATE 39 *I have more than four hundred paintings in the gallery, but there is room for only one behind my desk.*

PLATE 18 The day I see a hedge funder sipping cocktails on his yacht, adrift in the swamp adjacent to the sewage plant, which was the subject of the last painting he acquired, I will raise the white flag.

PLATE 31 *You may purchase this view of the Hudson at a price that is less than half the auction record for a Cropsey of a similar location.*

PLATE 30 A dealer takes considerable risk when declaring a painting a masterpiece. This is a masterpiece!

PLATE 40 *If you search auction and gallery catalogues of American paintings of the last ten years, it is nearly impossible to find a more significant work.*

PLATE 44 With extensive provenance, exhibitions at four major museums, and several pages of literary references, this is one of the most important paintings we have ever offered.

PLATE 24 *Robert Henri said, "This man is the biggest we have had since Winslow Homer."*

PLATE 36 "It expresses . . . so much and leaves so lively a play to the imagination." —*The New York Times*, 1894

"[P]ushed to great perfection . . . a superb and perfect example of the craft of the master." — ELLIOT DAINGERFIELD

Questroyal Storage Room
(one of eight)

OSCAR NIGHT - VANITY FAIR

DID YOU KNOW?

Questroyal is the only gallery ever to be invited to display paintings at the OSCARS

AND

we have been invited back in 2012.

Architectural Digest Greenroom
at the 83rd Annual Academy Awards,
created by renowned designer **Michael S. Smith**

Featured: Rockwell Kent's *Alpes-Maritimes*
courtesy of Questroyal Fine Art

Photo by Roger Davies for *Architectural Digest*

Works in the Catalogue

PLATE 1

Oscar Bluemner (1867–1938)

Downpour

Watercolor on paper

9 5/8 x 12 1/2 inches (sight size)

Signed lower right: *OFBLÜMNER* (artist's monogram)

PROVENANCE

Linda Hyman Fine Arts, New York

Heath Gallery, Inc., Atlanta

Michael N. Altman Fine Art & Advisory Services, LLC, New York

PLATE 2

Alexander Bower (1875–1952)

On the Cape, Near the Purpoodock Club, Maine

Oil on canvas

25 3/16 x 30 3/16 inches

Signed lower left: *ALEXANDER BOWER*; titled on verso: *ON THE CAPE, NEAR THE PURPOODOCK CLUB*

PROVENANCE

Avery Galleries, Haverford, Pennsylvania

The Cooley Gallery, Old Lyme, Connecticut

Questroyal Fine Art, LLC, New York

Private collection, New York

PLATE 3

Charles Ephraim Burchfield (1893–1967)

Backyard—Late Winter, 1916

Watercolor on paper

19 1/2 x 13 5/8 inches (sight size)

Signed and dated lower right: *–C E Burchfield–1916*

PROVENANCE

The artist

Mortimer Spiller, acquired directly from the above

ACA Galleries, New York

The Collection of Chris Huntington

Tom Veilleux Gallery, Portland, Maine

EXHIBITED

Portland Museum of Art, Maine, *The American Watercolor Tradition: Selections from the Collection,* June 13–September 3, 1995

PLATE 4

Charles Ephraim Burchfield (1893–1967)

Dead Trees in Southern Woods, 1918

Watercolor, gouache, and pencil on paper

12 x 9 inches

Signed lower right: *Chas Burchfield*; signed and dated lower left: *Chas Burchfield 1918*

PROVENANCE

Private collection, Glenview, Illinois

RELATED WORK

The First Hepaticas, 1917–1918, watercolor, gouache, and pencil on paper, 21 1/2 x 27 1/2 inches, The Museum of Modern Art, New York, gift of Abby Aldrich Rockefeller, 1935.

LITERATURE

Munson-Williams-Proctor Institute, *Charles Burchfield: Catalogue of Paintings in Public and Private Collections* (Utica, N.Y.: Munson-Williams-Proctor Institute, 1970), 82.

Note: This work was painted while the artist was in the army at Fort Jackson, South Carolina, from July 1918 to January 1919.

PLATE 5

John William Casilear (1811–1893)

Mountain River Landscape, 1868

Oil on canvas

12 1/4 x 10 1/4 inches

Signed and dated lower right: *JWC* (artist's monogram) *68*

PROVENANCE

Private collection

PLATE 6

George Cope (1855–1929)

Still Life with Berries, Sugar, and Cream Pitcher, 1916

Oil on canvas mounted on board

12 x 9 1/8 inches

Signed and dated: *GC* (artist's monogram) *'16*

PROVENANCE

Private collection, acquired directly from the artist

Sale, Alderfer Auction & Appraisal, December 9, 1999

Private collection, acquired from the above

Questroyal Fine Art, LLC, New York

Private collection, New Jersey

PLATE 7

Jasper Francis Cropsey (1823–1900)

Landscape with Trees, 1885

Oil on canvas

7 5/8 x 6 5/16 inches

Signed and dated lower right: *J. F. Cropsey 1885*

PROVENANCE

Private collection, by the 1970s

Private collection, by descent from the above

Note: This work will be included in the forthcoming catalogue raisonné of the artist's work by the Newington-Cropsey Foundation.

PLATE 8

Edward Alfred Cucuel (1875–1954)

Two Girls in White Beside a Lake in Autumn

Oil on canvas

31 9/16 x 31 3/4 inches

Signed lower right: *Cucuel*

PROVENANCE

Private collection, Germany

Guarisco Gallery, Washington, D.C.

Private collection, Washington, D.C.

PLATE 9

Thomas Doughty (1793–1856)

Sublime Landscape

Oil on canvas mounted to board

14 1/8 x 17 5/8 inches

Signed lower left: *DOUGHTY*

PROVENANCE

Alexander Gallery, New York

PLATE 10

William James Glackens (1870–1938)

Four Fruits

Oil on panel

9 13/16 x 13 13/16 inches

Signed lower right: *W. Glak* (illegible); verso: *Susanna without the Elders*

PROVENANCE

The Jean and Alvin Snowiss Collection, Pennsylvania

EXHIBITED

Palmer Museum of Art, The Pennsylvania State University, *An Endless Panorama of Beauty: Selections from the Jean and Alvin Snowiss Collection of American Art,* November 12, 2002–May 16, 2003

LITERATURE

Joyce Henri Robinson, *An Endless Panorama of Beauty: Selections from the Jean and Alvin Snowiss Collection of American Art* (University Park, Pa.: Palmer Museum of Art, The Pennsylvania State University, 2002), 42–43.

PLATE 11

George Henry Hall (1825–1913)

Still Life with Flowers, 1861

Oil on artist's board

12 1/16 x 10 1/16 inches

Signed and dated lower left: *G.H. Hall. '61*

PROVENANCE

Private collection, New York

PLATE 12

Robert Henri (1865–1929)

Monhegan, Maine

Pastel on paper mounted to board

20 x 14 1/8 inches

Signed lower right: *Robert Henri*

PROVENANCE

Private collection, New York

RELATED WORK

Monhegan Woodlands, 1918, pastel on paper, 20 x 12 inches, Collection of the Schwartz Family.

PLATE 13

George Inness (1825–1894)

Study for the Catskills, ca. 1875

Oil on paper laid down on canvas
9 3/16 x 12 7/16 inches

PROVENANCE

With an antiques dealer at a show, possibly in Miami, 1989

Private collection, acquired 1989

Private collection, Chicago

RELATED WORKS

Catskill Mountains, 1870, oil on canvas, 48 3/4 x 72 5/8 inches, The Art Institute of Chicago, Edward B. Butler Collection, 1912.1623. Signed and dated lower left: *G. Inness 1870.*

Hudson Valley, Midsummer, 1875, oil on canvas, 20 1/4 x 30 1/2 inches, Private collection. Signed and dated lower left: *G. Inness 1875.*

Midsummer, Hudson Valley, ca. 1875, oil on canvas, 12 x 18 1/16 inches, Present owner unknown.

LITERATURE

Michael Quick, *George Inness: A Catalogue Raisonné, Volume One, 1841–1879* (New Brunswick, N.J., and London: Rutgers University Press, 2007), 478–479, no. 538.

PLATE 14

Leon Kroll (1884–1974)

May at Woodstock, 1924

Oil on canvas

20 1/4 x 24 3/16 inches

Signed and dated lower right: *Leon Kroll 1924*; titled and signed on verso: *May at Woodstock, Leon Kroll*

PROVENANCE

Frank K. M. Rehn Galleries, New York

Private collection, acquired from the above

Private collection, acquired from the above, 1980

Private collection, New York

EXHIBITED

New Society of Artists, Frank K. M. Rehn Galleries, New York

PLATE 15

Anna Mary Robertson "Grandma" Moses (1860–1961)

Now We Can Skate

Oil on board

5 11/16 x 7 9/16 inches

Signed lower left: *MOSES.*; titled and inscribed on verso: *now we can Skate, no 1357,*

PROVENANCE

Galerie St. Etienne, New York

Collection of Ala Story

Private collection, acquired early 1950s

Sale, Sotheby's, New York, September 26, 1996, lot 181

Private collection, Illinois

LITERATURE

Otto Kallir, *Grandma Moses* (New York: Harry N. Abrams, Inc., 1973), 305.

PLATE 16

Albert Bierstadt (1830–1902)

Sea and Sky

Oil on paper mounted on board

14 1/8 x 18 1/4 inches

Signed lower right: *ABierstadt* (artist's monogram)

PROVENANCE

The Knight estate, Akron, Ohio, acquired ca. 1920s

RELATED WORK

Albert Bierstadt, *Beach Scene,* ca. 1871–1873, oil on paper mounted to fiberboard, 19 1/4 x 24 1/4 inches, The Seattle Art Museum, Gift of Mrs. John McCone in memory of Ada E. Pigott, 69.107.

LITERATURE

Elizabeth Wilson, review of "The Nature of a Nation: Paintings of the Hudson River School" (Questroyal Fine Art, LLC), *ARTnews* 107, no. 5 (May 2008): 149.

Mona Molarsky, review of "An Untamed Nation" (Questroyal Fine Art, LLC), *ARTnews* 110, no. 6 (June 2011): 106.

PLATE 17

Thomas Cole (1801–1848)

On Catskill Creek, 1836

Oil on canvas

20 5/8 x 15 11/16 inches

Signed, inscribed, and dated on verso panel: *Thomas Cole Catskill 1836*

PROVENANCE

Alexander Gallery, New York

PLATE 18

Samuel Colman (1832–1920)

Morning, 1859

Oil on canvas

15 1/4 x 24 3/16 inches

Signed and dated lower right: *S. Colman '59*

PROVENANCE

Kenneth Lux Gallery, New York

Private collection, New York

Private collection, Connecticut

EXHIBITED

Kenneth Lux Gallery, New York, *Nineteenth-century American Paintings,* November 15–December 10, 1977

LITERATURE

Nineteenth-century American Paintings (New York: Kenneth Lux Gallery, 1977), n.p., no. 5.

PLATE 19

Jasper Francis Cropsey (1823–1900)

A Cabin on Greenwood Lake, 1879

Oil on canvas

9 7/16 x 16 3/8 inches

Signed and dated lower right: *J. F. Cropsey 1879*

PROVENANCE

Possibly, Sale, Butterfield's, San Francisco, June 21, 1984, lot 2092

Mrs. John C. Newington, by 1990

Mr. Richard Weimer, Darien, Connecticut, 1990

Vose Galleries, Boston

Sale, Richard A. Bourne Co., Inc., Hyannis, Massachusetts, August 21, 1990, lot 178

Mrs. Benjamin Ross, Albany, New York

Sale, Christie's, New York, December 6, 1991, lot 75

Private collection, New York, acquired from the above

A New York estate, by descent

Note: This work will be included in the forthcoming catalogue raisonné of the artist's work by the Newington-Cropsey Foundation.

PROVENANCE

Mr. and Mrs. Orton P. Jackson, by 1949

The Pennsylvania Academy of the Fine Arts, gifted in the memory of Emily Penrose Jackson from the above, 1983

Private collection, New York

EXHIBITED

Pennsylvania Academy of the Fine Arts, Philadelphia, *A Growing American Treasure: Acquisitions since 1978,* September 21, 1984–April 14, 1985

Pennsylvania Academy of the Fine Arts, Philadelphia; Greenville County Museum of Art, North Carolina; Orlando Museum of Art, Florida; Akron Art Museum, Ohio; Memorial Art Gallery, Rochester, New York; Beaverbrook Art Gallery, New Brunswick, Canada; Huntsville Museum of Art, Alabama, *Light, Air, and Color: American Impressionist Paintings from the Collection of the Pennsylvania Academy of the Fine Arts,* June 8, 1990–July 25, 1993

Farnsworth Art Museum, Rockland, Maine, *Inventing Acadia: Artists and Tourists at Mount Desert,* June 13–October 24, 1999

LITERATURE

A Growing American Treasure: Acquisitions since 1978 (Philadelphia: Pennsylvania Academy of the Fine Arts, 1984), no. 60.

Susan Danly, *Light, Air, and Color: American Impressionist Paintings from the Collection of the Pennsylvania Academy of the Fine Arts* (Philadelphia: Pennsylvania Academy of the Fine Arts, 1990), 47, no. 20.

Pamela J. Belanger, *Inventing Acadia: Artists and Tourists at Mount Desert* (Rockland, Maine: The Farnsworth Art Museum, distributed by University Press of New England, 1999), 10, 14.

Note: This painting will be included in the forthcoming catalogue raisonné of the artist's work by Kathleen M. Burnside and Stuart P. Feld.

PLATE 43

Childe Hassam (1859–1935)

Frenchman's Bay, Mount Desert, 1896

Oil on canvas

26 1/8 x 36 1/4 inches

Signed and dated lower right: *Childe Hassam·1896*; signed, titled, and dated on verso: *Frenchman's Bay C.H. 1896*

PROVENANCE

The artist, 1896

Mr. Newman E. Montross, New York, likely from the artist, until 1919

Sale, American Art Galleries, New York, February 27, 1919, no. 43

N. Wheelock, acquired from the above, 1919

Returned to the artist (presumably), by bequest to the American Academy of Arts and Letters, New York, 1935–1963

Milch Galleries, New York, 1963–1965

Gilbert P. Schafer, Cleveland, 1965

Private collection, by descent from the above

Hirschl & Adler Galleries, New York

Questroyal Fine Art, LLC, New York

Private collection, Pennsylvania

RELATED WORKS

Looking over Frenchman's Bay at Green Mountain, 1896, oil on canvas, 26 5/16 x 35 7/8 inches, Questroyal Fine Art, LLC, New York.*

Sunset, Ironbound Island, 1896, oil on canvas, 26 x 30 inches, Location unknown.

Note: *Frenchman's Bay, Mount Desert* will be included in forthcoming catalogue raisonné of the artist's work by Kathleen M. Burnside and Stuart P. Feld.

* *Looking over Frenchman's Bay at Green Mountain* was acquired from The Pennsylvania Academy of the Fine Arts, Philadelphia.

PLATE 44

Childe Hassam (1859–1935)

Hollyhocks, Isle of Shoals, 1902

Pastel on paper

17 7/8 x 22 1/16 inches

Signed and dated lower left: *Childe Hassam. 1902*

PROVENANCE

Collection of the artist, until 1935

American Academy of Arts and Letters, New York, by bequest of the artist, 1935

The Milch Galleries, New York, 1951

Mr. John Fox, Boston, acquired from the above, 1951

Mr. Dwight M. Collins, business partner of the above

By descent in the family

Sale, C.G. Sloan & Co., Washington, D.C., June 3–5, 1983, lot 1803

Spanierman Gallery, LLC, New York, acquired at the above sale

Private collection, Colorado and Houston, acquired from the above, early 1990s

EXHIBITED

Yale University Art Gallery, New Haven; Denver Art Museum; Smithsonian American Art Museum, *Childe Hassam: An Island Garden Revisited,* April 4, 1990–January 7, 1991

Museum of Fine Arts, Houston, *American Painters in the Age of Impressionism,* December 4, 1994–March 26, 1995

Adelson Galleries, New York; Meredith Long &. Company, Houston, *Childe Hassam: An American Impressionist,* November 2, 1999–February 5, 2000

LITERATURE

David Park Curry, *Childe Hassam: An Island Garden Revisited* (New York: W. W. Norton & Co.; Denver: Denver Art Museum, 1990), 66–70.

Emily Ballew Neff and George T. M. Shackelford, *American Painters in the Age of Impressionism* (Houston: The Museum of Fine Arts, 1994), 44–45, 113.

Warren Adelson, Jay E. Cantor, and William H. Gerdts, *Childe Hassam: An American Impressionist* (New York: Adelson Galleries, 1999), no. 62.

Note: This pastel will be included in the forthcoming catalogue raisonné of the artist's work by Kathleen M. Burnside and Stuart P. Feld. Notably, David Park Curry identified the pictured view as the southwest corner of Celia Thaxter's garden. Thaxter, Hassam's patron and muse until her death in 1894, was an important figure in the artist's life and career. *Hollyhocks, Isle of Shoals,* created eight years after her death, can thus be seen as a poignant tribute to her.